THE ULTIMATE DINOSAUR ACTIVITY BOOK!

THE ULTIMATE DINOSAUR ACTIVITY BOOK!

THIS BOOK BELONGS TO

. . . .

DINOSAURS ARE AWESOME!

ONE OF THE COOLEST THINGS

ABOUT DINOSAURS IS THAT EVEN THOUGH THESE PREHISTORIC CREATURES LIVED MILLIONS OF YEARS AGO, SCIENTISTS ARE CONSTANTLY DISCOVERING NEW THINGS ABOUT THEM BY UNCOVERING FOSSILS. THESE FOSSIL SPECIALISTS, CALLED PALEONTOLOGISTS, HAVE IDENTIFIED MORE THAN 700 UNIQUE SPECIES SO FAR! READ ON AND SEE WHAT AMAZING FACTS YOU CAN DIG UP ABOUT DINOSAURS!

Test your dino knowledge with tons of fun-filled activities, games, puzzles and more!

MYTH
DINOSAURS WERE BAD PARENTS AND LONERS

After hatching out of their eggs, baby dinosaurs had weak bones and couldn't get food on their own! Fortunately, their parents collected food and brought it back to the nest for their babies. Fossil evidence of a Philydrosauras, a dinosaur-like reptile that lived during the Jurassic Period, shows an adult Philydrosauras surrounded by its six children, leading some scientists to conclude that dinosaur families were also close to each other!

EGG-XACTLY!

Not all dinosaur nests were the same! Researchers believe some eggs, such as those of the Brachiosaurus, were buried underground by their parents (to better hide them from predators!) while others had nests out in the open!

PALEONTOLOGIST PUZZLE

No two dinosaurs have the same name.

DINOSAUR EXPERTS SEARCH ALL OVER THE WORLD FOR FOSSILS—
HOW MANY SPECIES CAN YOU FIND IN THIS WORD SEARCH?
YOU CAN SEARCH FROM LEFT TO RIGHT, TOP TO BOTTOM OR DIAGONALLY.
CIRCLE THE WORDS WHEN YOU FIND THEM

```
X A P A T O S A U R U S
T Y A A W G L Q B J B U
D R R V I S Q Z V R X R
Q Q K E C G V Y O R J U
B L S S T Z N N I R J A
B C O O I P T I S W G S
J Q S H K O I S M B R O
R Y A P M U I D M O W N
V F U E A S T A U Y N I
S U R U A S O R D A H P
K U U V R R L G B W C S
S A S U M I M Y P R A H
```

WORD BANK

BRONTOMERUS
HADROSAURUS
SPINOSAURUS
NOMINGIA
APATOSAURUS

CAUDIPTERYX
HARPYMIMUS
PARKSOSAURUS

ANSWERS ON PAGE 55

9

Evidence from fossils strongly suggests the T. rex would eat the Triceratops when given a chance, but it's unknown if the predator would fight a fully grown Triceratops or just scavenge one that had already died.

MYTH
DINOSAURS ONLY LIVED ON LAND

FUN FACT!

ONE OF THE ANIMALS THE SPINOSAURUS LIKED TO DINE ON WOULD LOOK FAMILIAR TO PEOPLE TODAY—SHARKS! SHARKS HAVE BEEN ON EARTH FOR ALMOST 450 MILLION YEARS, AND THE SHARKS WE SEE TODAY ARE DESCENDANTS OF THE SPECIES THAT SURVIVED THE EXTINCTION EVENT THAT WIPED OUT THE DINOSAURS.

Dinosaurs were the biggest creatures to walk the Earth, but that doesn't mean that's the only place they roamed. The Spinosaurus was a semi-aquatic dinosaur, meaning it lived both on land and in the water. So far, it is the only dinosaur we've found that adapted for swimming. In 1912, a Spinosaurus fossil found in Egypt by a German paleontologist named Ernst Freiherr Stromer von Reichenbach showed the dinosaur's jaw and mouth had very unusual teeth. They were most likely used for catching fish!

SPOT THE DIFFERENCE

CAN YOU FIND THE FOUR DIFFERENCES BETWEEN THESE PICTURES?

ANSWERS ON PAGE 55

MYTH
DINOSAURS WERE ALL COLD-BLOODED

It's still a relatively new theory, but many scientists believe some dinosaurs were cold-blooded, while others weren't! Cold-blooded animals can't produce their own body heat. All reptiles are cold-blooded, and so are frogs and fish. It's long been assumed dinosaurs were reptiles, and so it was assumed they were cold-blooded. But new research suggests some dinosaurs were able to control their body temperature (just like you)! Knowing that birds, who are warm-blooded, descended from dinosaurs, it makes sense to think some dinosaurs were warm-blooded too. See? Even some of the smartest scientists on Earth are wrong sometimes....

FUN FACT!
SCIENTISTS REFER TO COLD-BLOODED ANIMALS AS POIKILOTHERMS [POY-KEE-LOW-THERMS].

STEGOSAURUS MAZE

DESPITE ITS SIZE, THIS DINOSAUR HAD A BRAIN THE SIZE OF A PING-PONG BALL. SHOW OFF HOW BIG YOUR BRAIN IS BY COMPLETING THIS MAZE!

Stegosaurus lived during the Jurassic period.

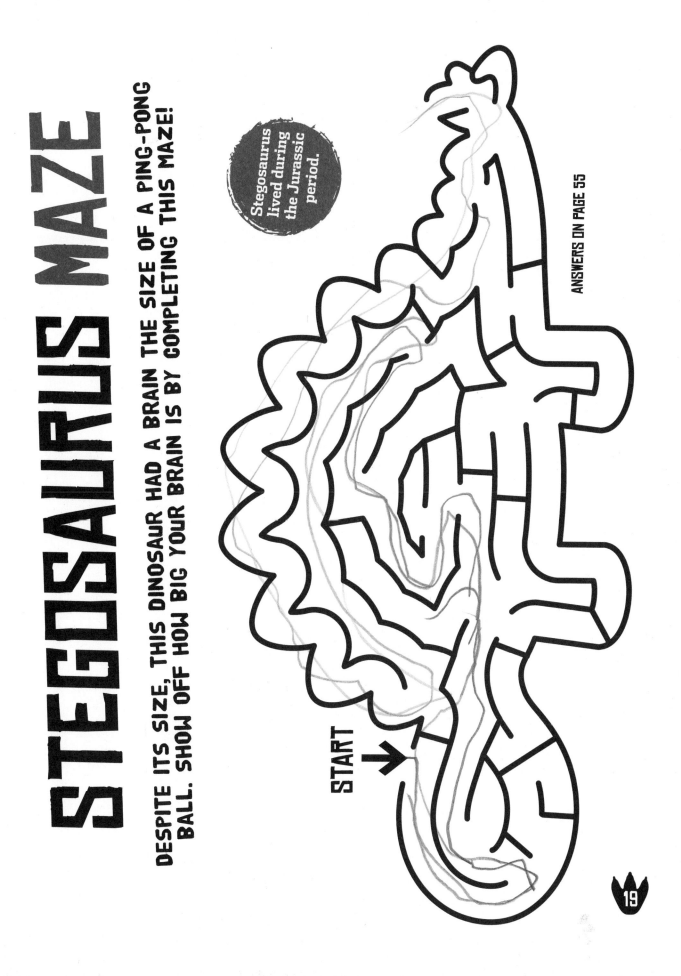

START

ANSWERS ON PAGE 55

19

MYTH
DINOSAURS ARE COMPLETELY EXTINCT

Although flying reptiles called Pterosaurs lived alongside dinosaurs, modern birds descended from small dinos that could fly.

It's true you won't see any dinos walking around today, but many scientists feel modern birds are directly descended from a group of theropod dinosaurs known as maniraptoran theropods. Dinosaurs belonging to this group include the Velociraptor, a small, meat-eating predator made famous by Hollywood movies. So the next time you see a pigeon, just think of how scary his ancestors were millions of years ago!

FUN FACT!

TODAY, MANY SCIENTISTS AND RESEARCHERS BELIEVE SOME SPECIES OF DINOSAURS WERE COVERED IN FEATHERS. THOUGH THERE'S STILL DISAGREEMENT OVER HOW MANY SPECIES HAD FEATHERS VS. SCALES.

21

DRAW THAT DINO!

REVEAL THE DINOSAUR BY CONNECTING THE DOTS.

ANSWERS ON PAGE 57

23

MYTH
DINOSAUR FOSSILS ARE JUST OLD BONES IN THE GROUND

Fossils are actually imprints of a bone! They aren't the bone itself, but are like a picture of it instead. Over the millions of years the dinosaur's body is underground, its skin wears away and only the hard parts—like bones, teeth and horns—are left over. Then, water from the surrounding rocks underground breaks down the bones until there is nothing left. This leaves a hole, or image, preserving the shape of the bones. Over time, sediment and water fill the hole and hardens, leaving a fossil. This is a very lengthy process—it takes millions of years for fossils to form!

FUN FACT!

Bones aren't the only kind of remains that can be preserved as fossils. Ancient remains of footprints, nests, leaves and even teeth have also been uncovered by paleontologists, the scientists who dig for fossils.

25

MYTH
DINOSAURS ALL ROARED

No matter what you see in the movies, dinosaurs most likely did not roar! Birds, crocodiles and alligators are the closest living relatives that might give us clues to how dinosaurs sounded. Most birds vocalize through their syrinx, which is located in their throat. They also have a flesh sac called an esophageal pouch, which allows birds with large bodies to make low murmurs. Crocodiles and alligators vocalize using their larynx, a soft-tissue structure located in their throat. But none of them roar, which means dinos probably didn't either!

FUN FACT!

ALTHOUGH DINOS MAY NOT HAVE LET OUT MIGHTY ROARS, THAT DOESN'T MEAN THEY WERE COMPLETELY SILENT. THINK OF HOW MUCH NOISE A GOOSE CAN MAKE BY HONKING. NOW IMAGINE THE SAME NOISE COMING OUT OF A T. REX!

Some scientists believe large dinosaurs could whip their large tails so fast, it created a loud "crack" used for communication!

PTERODACTYL PTROUBLE

ONE OF THESE DINOSAURS ISN'T LIKE THE OTHERS. SPOT THE PTERODACTYL THAT DOESN'T FIT IN!

ANSWERS ON PAGE 57

MYTH
DINOSAURS WERE AT THE TOP OF THE FOOD CHAIN

ome animals living during the Age of the Dinosaurs looked at dinos as a delicious meal! The Deinosuchus was a prehistoric crocodile that would chomp on dinosaurs that would come too close to the river. There was also the Quetzalcatlus, which belonged to the Pterosaurs family, also known as the winged lizards. They had a minimum wingspan of 35 feet, potentially weighing up to 550 pounds, and preyed on many types of dinosaurs!

RIBBIT RUMBLER

One of the weirdest predators of dinosaurs was an ancient frog called *Beelzebufo ampinga*, which weighed up to 10 pounds! This amphibian most likely snacked on any baby dinosaurs unlucky enough to cross its path!

MYTH
DINOSAURS ALL LIVED DURING THE SAME TIME AND IN THE SAME PLACE

When dinosaurs walked the Earth, they roamed at different periods in history. The Mesozoic Era, also known as the Age of Dinosaurs, included three time periods: the Triassic, Jurassic and Cretaceous Periods. This means that some dinosaurs lived earlier than others. For example, the Stegosaurus lived during the Jurassic Period and would never have interacted with the Triceratops, a dinosaur that lived during the Cretaceous Period. Different dinosaurs lived in different parts of the world too. The T. rex and the Velociraptor lived continents apart!

The name "Triceratops" means "three-horned face," which makes a lot of sense when you look at one!

FUN FACT!
THOUGH FOSSILS HAVE BEEN FOUND ALL OVER THE PLANET, MORE THAN 5,000 HAVE BEEN UNCOVERED IN THE UNITED STATES, MAKING AMERICA THE LEADER IN DINO FOSSILS!

MYTH

THE DINOSAUR SKELETONS YOU SEE AT THE MUSEUM ARE REAL BONES

Real dinosaur fossils are way too fragile and heavy to display, so when you go to a museum, you are most likely looking at casts of the fossils instead! Real fossils are used as a mold to cast the replicas. Because these fossils are real, and from real dinosaurs, the casts look like real bones!

THE TITANOSAUR

FUN FACT!

THE LARGEST REPLICA SKELETON OF A DINOSAUR ON DISPLAY IS A TITANOSAUR AT THE AMERICAN MUSEUM OF NATURAL HISTORY IN NEW YORK. IT'S 122 FEET LONG AND MORE THAN 19 FEET HIGH. WOW!

DINO DOOR HANGER!

SHOW OFF THE DINOSAUR YOU LOVE MOST WITH THIS DINO DOOR HANGER! COLOR AND CUT OUT THE HANGER AND ADD A FRIEND!

MYTH
DINOSAURS ALL LIVED IN A HOT, JUNGLE ENVIRONMENT

As the continents separated, dinosaurs became more diverse while different species evolved on different landmasses.

FUN FACT!

ANTARCTICA WASN'T ALWAYS ICY AND COLD. DURING MOST OF THE TRIASSIC AND JURASSIC PERIODS, THE CONTINENT WAS A TROPICAL FOREST.

Dinosaurs lived in many different climates! During the Triassic Period, many dinosaurs lived near riversides and scrublands. Shallow riversides were covered with ferns and horsetail plants. Scrublands were semi-desert plains filled with plants that could survive with a lack of water supply. During the Jurassic Period, vegetation grew particularly lush! During the Cretaceous Period, the seas expanded, separating continents and causing diversity of plants and animals. From swamplands to desert plains and even to mountains, dinosaurs roamed everywhere!

MY FAVORITE DINO

THERE ARE MORE THAN 700 KNOWN KINDS OF DINOSAURS! SHOW OFF YOUR DINO KNOWLEDGE BY WRITING ABOUT YOUR THREE FAVORITE SPECIES BELOW!

1

MY FAVORITE DINOSAUR IS THE _____

IT MOSTLY ATE _____

I LIKE IT BECAUSE _____

IF I HAD IT FOR A PET, I WOULD _____

2

MY SECOND FAVORITE DINOSAUR IS THE _____

IT MOSTLY ATE _____

I LIKE IT BECAUSE _____

IF I HAD IT FOR A PET, I WOULD _____

3

MY THIRD FAVORITE DINOSAUR IS THE _____

IT MOSTLY ATE _____

I LIKE IT BECAUSE _____

IF I HAD IT FOR A PET, I WOULD _____

41

MYTH
DINOSAURS WERE ALL HUGE!

The Utahraptor (discovered in the state of Utah) was one of the largest raptors we've found, measuring around 18 feet in length!

ALL SHAPES AND SIZES

Even when dinos were related, they could be extremely different—just like humans. The Dilong, a member of the same family as T. rex, weighed only about 25 pounds. T. rex could weigh up to 15,000 pounds!

Dinosaurs came in all shapes and sizes. Even though the T. rex was one of the largest and most ferocious dinosaurs ever to roam the Earth (reaching up to 20 feet tall!), that doesn't mean all dinosaurs were big and scary. Dinosaurs like the Gargoyleosaurus and the Velociraptor only stood around 3 feet tall!

FUN FACT!
A RELATIVE OF THE VELOCIRAPTOR, THE MICRORAPTOR WAS A DINOSAUR THAT WAS ONLY ABOUT 2 FEET LONG. THE SMALLEST RAPTOR WE'VE DISCOVERED SO FAR, MICRORAPTOR LOOKED A LOT LIKE A BIG PIGEON.

DINO WORD SEARCH

CAN YOU FIND THE DINOSAUR-RELATED WORDS HIDDEN BELOW?

```
T Y R A N N O S A U R U S R E X
V W K H L A V D B B B E U Q B J
X E O W D I R X K A M I Q B W U
H U L N Q I S R N N H S N C B R
F X N O B E E S J T Y T X T L A
G U C S C P G B O N E U J B A S
J D K E T I O G Z F V F Z Q N S
O B I I M B R K S C S S F L F I
P Q L F U I N A L R L Q Y T R C
W E Q W E F C W P R O W B T N I
X T Y F S E L X L T E J J Q G P
R Z T T U P M V E N O F E P Y C
E U D T M D P Z N X G R L B S V
V U H T C N I T X E C L X B K T
N X B K Z V V S M D Q L D S P T
X Q J G E X P P F S R F F O T C
```

WORD BANK

TYRANNOSAURUS
REX
REPTILE
BIRD
EXTINCT

FOSSIL
MUSEUM
BONE
VELOCIRAPTOR
JURASSIC
EGGS

ANSWERS ON PAGE 57

45

MYTH
DINOSAURS AND HUMANS LIVED AT THE SAME TIME

Sadly, dinosaurs and humans only lived together in the world of fiction! When dinosaurs existed about 65 million years ago, humans weren't riding them to work like Fred Flintstone because we didn't exist yet. Scientists believe the first human-like ancestor appeared between 5 to 6 million years ago, meaning dinosaurs are much older than us and went extinct long before we walked the Earth.

MAMMALS AND DINOS

Just because humans and dinosaurs didn't live together on Earth, it doesn't mean the reptiles had the planet to themselves. Scientists believe mammals, warm-blooded animals with fur that drink milk and don't lay eggs, first appeared about 200 million years ago. The mammals that existed during the Age of the Dinosaurs (like cronopio, pictured) were mostly small creatures that survived by eating insects, other animals and even dinosaur eggs! Talk about a big omelette!

CROSSWORD QUEST

FIND ALL EIGHT DINOSAUR-RELATED WORDS USING YOUR DINO KNOWLEDGE!

ACROSS
2. An imprint of a bone found in the ground
4. The first time period of the Dino Era
7. The final time period of the Dino Era
8. These animals evolved from dinosaurs

DOWN
1. The most dino fossils have been found in North _____
3. Smaller version of Velociraptor
4. This big meat-eater lived during the Cretaceous Period
5. Legless, cold-blooded animal
6. The middle time period of the Dino Era

ANSWERS ON PAGE 59

TEST TIME!

HOW MUCH DO YOU KNOW ABOUT THE AGE OF DINOSAURS? FILL IN THE BLANKS!

1. The three time periods that make up the Mesozoic Era are Jurassic, _____ and Cretaceous.

2. The Stegosaurus lived during the _____ Period.

3. The T. rex and the _____ lived very far apart!

ANSWERS ON PAGE 59

DINOSAUR MYTHS DEBUNKED!

USING WHAT YOU KNOW ABOUT DINOSAURS, CAN YOU SOLVE THIS QUIZ? CIRCLE YOUR ANSWERS!

1. The T. rex was an herbivore.
TRUE
FALSE

2. Triceratops is famous for the four horns on its head.
TRUE
FALSE

3. Nearly everything we know about dinosaurs is because of the fossils they left behind.
TRUE
FALSE

4. The word "dinosaur" comes from the Greek words for "terrible" and "lizard."
TRUE
FALSE

5. The Quetzalcatlus had a minimum wingspan of 35 feet.
TRUE
FALSE

6. All dinosaurs roared.
TRUE
FALSE

7. The closest living relatives to dinosaurs today are birds, crocodiles and alligators.
TRUE
FALSE

ANSWERS ON PAGE 59

ANSWER KEY

PAGE 9
WORD SEARCH

PAGE 15
SPOT THE DIFFERENCE

PAGE 19
STEGOSAURUS MAZE

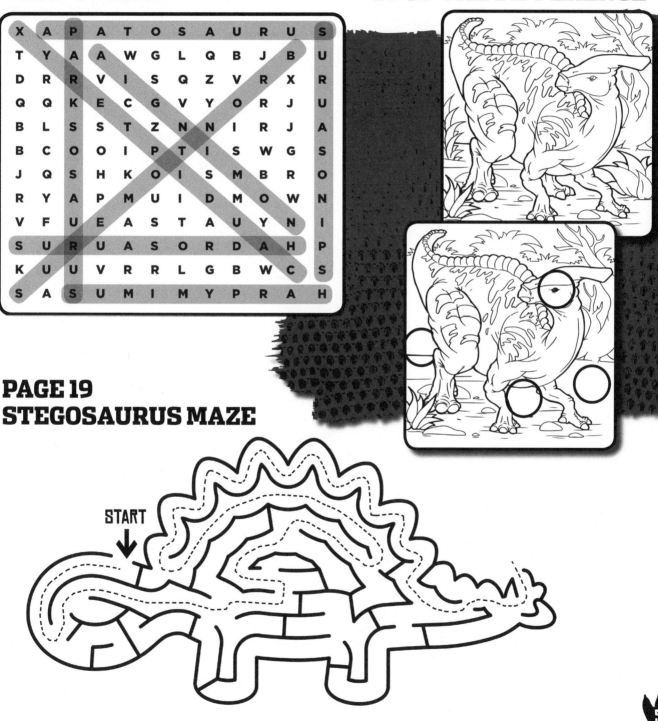

START

ANSWER KEY

PAGE 23
DRAW
THAT
DINO!

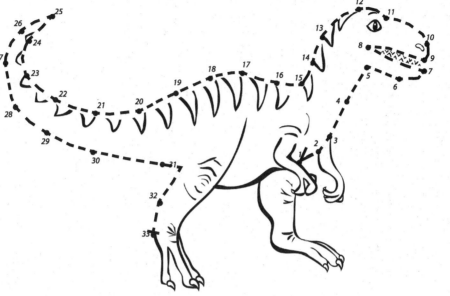

PAGE 29
PTERODACTYL
PTROUBLE

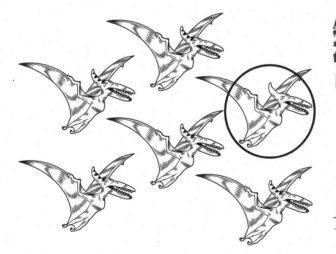

PAGE 45
WORD SEARCH

ANSWER KEY

PAGE 49
CROSSWORD QUEST

Crossword solution:

- 1. AMERICA (down)
- 2. FOSSIL (across)
- 3. MICRORAPTOR (down)
- 4. TRIASSIC (across)
- 5. SNAKE (down)
- 6. TREX (down)
- 7. CRETACEOUS (across)
- 8. JURASSIC (down)
- 8. BIRDS (across)

PAGE 51
TEST TIME!

1. The three time periods that make up the Mesozoic Era are Jurassic, **Triassic** and Cretaceous.

2. The Stegosaurus lived during the **Jurassic** Period.

3. The T. rex and the **Velociraptor** lived very far apart!

PAGE 53
DINOSAUR MYTHS DEBUNKED

1. FALSE
2. FALSE
3. TRUE
4. TRUE
5. TRUE
6. FALSE
7. TRUE

DINOSAUR OF A DIFFERENT COLOR

USE COLORFUL CRAYONS, PENS, PENCILS, MARKERS AND YOUR IMAGINATION TO MAKE THESE DINOS POP!

Paleontologists can study fossils at the microscopic level to determine what color the dinosaur that left it might have been.

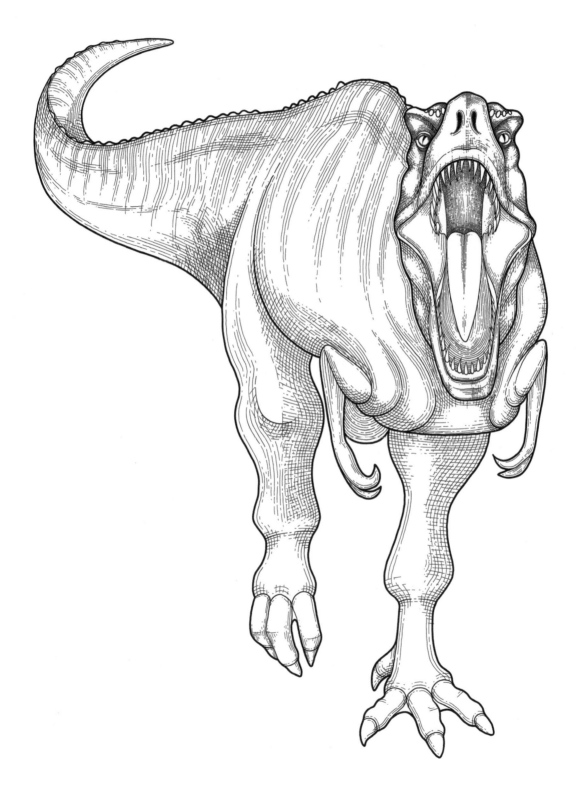

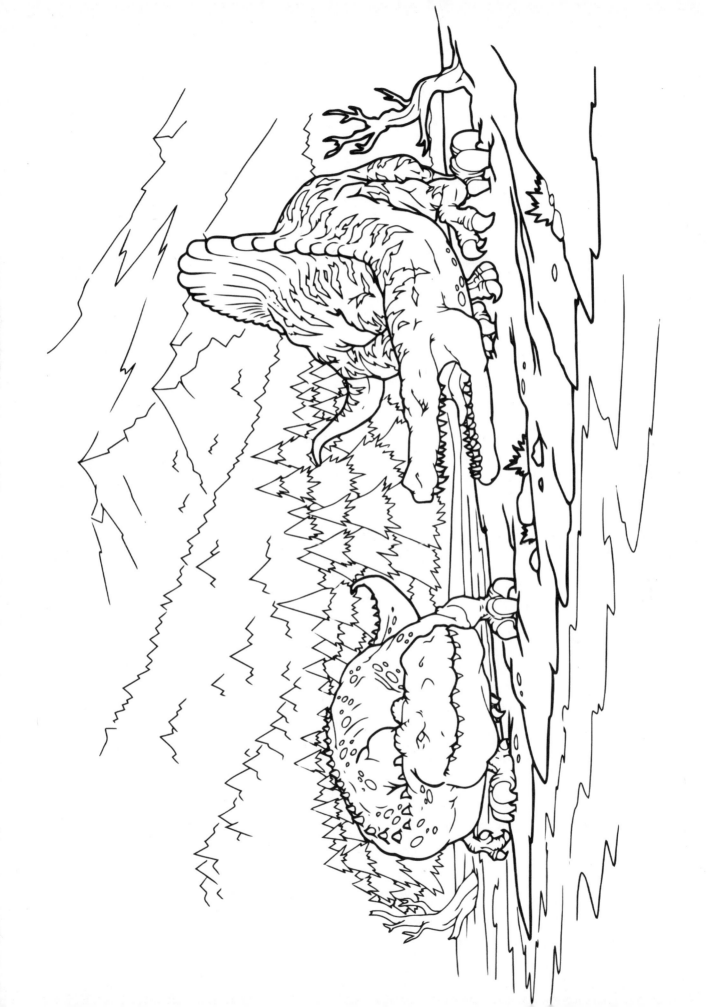

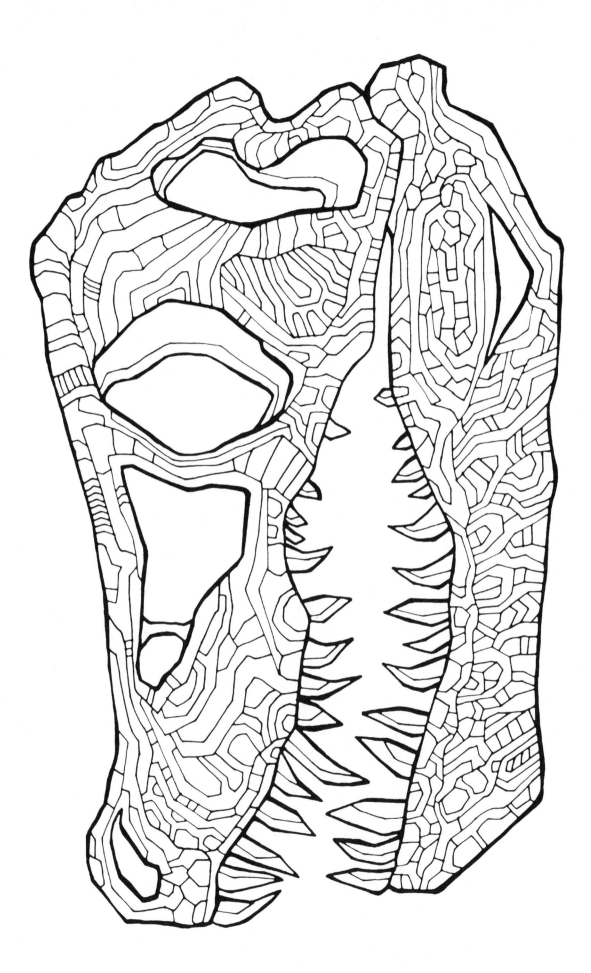

Topix Media Lab
For inquiries, call 646-838-6637

Copyright 2021 Topix Media Lab

Published by Topix Media Lab
14 Wall Street, Suite 4B
New York, NY 10005

Printed in the U.S.

ISBN-13: 978-1-948174-50-3
ISBN-10: 1-948174-50-2

CEO Tony Romando

Vice President & Publisher Phil Sexton
Senior Vice President of Sales & New Markets Tom Mifsud
Vice President of Retail Sales & Logistics Linda Greenblatt
Director of Finance Vandana Patel
Manufacturing Director Nancy Puskuldjian
Financial Analyst Matthew Quinn

Chief Content Officer Jeff Ashworth
Director of Editorial Operations Courtney Kerrigan
Creative Director Steven Charny
Photo Director Dave Weiss
Executive Editor Tim Baker

Content Editor Juliana Sharaf
Art Director Susan Dazzo
Associate Photo Editor Catherine Armanasco
Senior Editor Trevor Courneen
Copy Editor & Fact Checker Benjamin VanHoose
Designer Kelsey Payne

Co-Founders Bob Lee, Tony Romando

COVER: Shutterstock

All images Shutterstock except: p35 Storms Media Group/Alamy

TM21-02